C000235087

John Wright spent his childhood in Rugby, Warwickshire. He then took a degree in Zoology at the University of Wales, Bangor, and stayed on to do a Ph.D in Freshwater Ecology before undertaking further research in Manitoba, Canada. After returning to England, he joined a research team at the University of Reading engaged in long-term studies on the ecology of chalk streams in southern England. In 1977 he was appointed to the staff of the River Laboratory at East Stoke near Wareham, Dorset. During the next few years he and his colleagues developed a novel approach for assessing the biological quality of rivers, based on the invertebrate fauna, and in 1990 this technique was adopted by Government Agencies for use throughout the United Kingdom. He has written 75 scientific papers and many more contract reports during his professional career. In addition, he has a wide-ranging interest in Natural History and is an active member of the Dorset Wildlife Trust.

Following page
A grey heron stands motionless, watching for movement
in the shallows. After the breeding season, herons disperse
to lakes, rivers and associated wetlands to search for
fish and other items of food.

DISCOVER DORSET

RIVERS AND STREAMS

JOHN WRIGHT

THE DOVECOTE PRESS

For my father, Rowan, who spent his early life in Dorset
and first introduced me to this very special part of England.

Brown trout are common in many of Dorset's fast-flowing
rivers and streams. This juvenile trout displays dark lateral
patches known as parr marks.

First published in 2003 by The Dovecote Press Ltd
Stanbridge, Wimborne, Dorset BH21 4JD

ISBN 1 904349 10 2

Series designed by Humphrey Stone

Typeset in Monotype Sabon
Printed and bound in Singapore

A CIP catalogue record for this book is available
from the British Library

1 3 5 7 9 8 6 4 2

CONTENTS

THE VARIETY OF RIVERS IN DORSET 7

PLANTS 20

INVERTEBRATES 29

FISH 40

BIRDS 47

MAMMALS 55

THE MANAGEMENT OF RIVERS IN DORSET 60

VISITING RIVERS AND STREAMS 69

FURTHER READING 72

ACKNOWLEDGEMENTS 75

INDEX 76

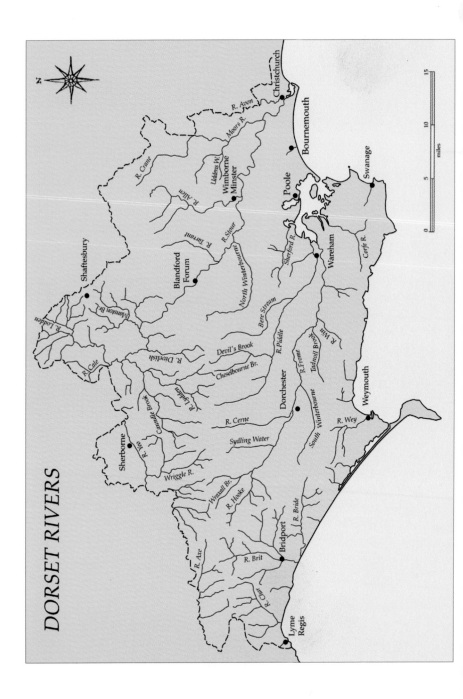

DORSET RIVERS

N

Christchurch
R. Avon
Moors R.
Bournemouth
Uddens W.
Wimborne
Minster
R. Crane
R. Allen
Poole
Swanage
R. Tarrant
R. Stour
Sherford R.
Shaftesbury
North Winterbourne
Wareham
Corfe R.
Blandford
Forum
Bere Stream
R. Loddon
Manston Br.
R. Piddle
R. Win
R. Cale
Devil's Brook
R. Divelish
Tadnoll Brook
R. Frome
Weymouth
Cheselbourne Br.
R. Lydden
Dorchester
Caundle Brook
R. Cerne
South Winterbourne
R. Wey
R. Yeo
Sherborne
Sydling Water
Wriggle R.
Winxall Br.
R. Hooke
R. Bride
Bridport
R. Axe
R. Brit
R. Char
Lyme
Regis

0   5   10   15
miles

THE VARIETY OF RIVERS IN DORSET

To the naturalist, a stream or river adds a special element to the landscape and the opportunity to observe and enjoy a wide variety of plants and animals associated with water. Even an unhurried look from a bridge or a leisurely walk along a river bank can start to work its magic. How can the plants we see, together with the invertebrates and fish survive in this watery environment which is literally flowing past them to the sea? When we glimpse a trout taking an emerging mayfly or a dragonfly patrolling its bankside territory we are reminded that this complex ecosystem links water, land and air.

From source to mouth, the only certainty about a river is that it flows one way, gathering tributaries as it drains a progressively larger area. Throughout this journey the temperature and flow regime, the slope and substratum, and many other features, tend to show progressive changes downstream, allowing the development of a sequence of habitat types, each with its own characteristic plants and animals.

The basic features of all river systems are determined by the local geology, climate and topography, and further influenced by man's use of the catchment. The many different geological formations in Dorset, from the older Jurassic rocks in the north and west, through the central outcrop of Cretaceous chalk to the younger Tertiary deposits of the Poole Basin in the east, are responsible for the variety of our rivers. The climate is mid-temperate with a maritime influence and the modest rainfall of around 900 millimetres together with the rounded topography of the chalk, ensures that most of the rivers are essentially lowland in character.

The drainage patterns for the Frome, Piddle and Stour, which represent Dorset's three major river systems are all in a south-easterly direction. The Frome and Piddle, both fine examples of chalk streams, pour into Poole Harbour, whilst the Stour, which drains more complex geology, flows into Christchurch Harbour.

For naturalists and fishermen alike, the mention of a chalk stream conjures up a vision of crystal-clear water where trout lie motionless between beds of swirling green weed. To understand why these streams give such a clear view of life below the water surface, we need to trace them to their source within the chalk itself. When rain falls on chalk downland, a high proportion of the water flows directly through the soil and into the underlying chalk, instead of running directly off the land. Chalk is porous, but full of cracks and fissures, so the water

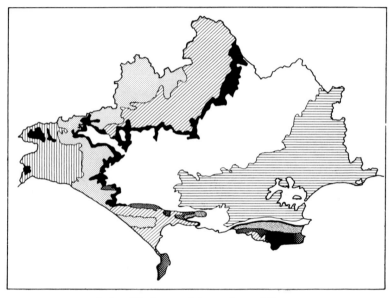

A simplified map of the geology of Dorset.

Tertiary rocks (clays, sands & gravels).

Chalk (limestone).

Lower Greensand, Gault & Upper Greensand (clays & sands).

Wealden (clays, silts, sands & grits).

Portland Sand & Stone & Purbeck Limestone Group (limestones & clays).

Kellaways Beds, Oxford Clay, Corallian & Kimmeridge Clay (limestones & clays).

Inferior Oolite, Fuller's Earth, Frome Clay, Forest Marble & Cornbrash (limestone & clays).

Lower, Middle & Upper Lias (thin limestones, clays, silts & sands).

Water crowfoot in flower on the River Frome at Bradford Peverell, upstream of Dorchester, where it flows through open meadowland.

moves downwards to accumulate as a huge underground reservoir known as an aquifer. In practice, it takes a long time for this groundwater to move down through the chalk and then laterally to emerge in the form of springs. As a result, chalk streams have several distinctive characteristics.

Firstly, they have a relatively stable flow regime. Winter rains normally replenish the aquifer to give peak stream flows in late winter and early spring, before the flow gradually decreases through the summer and autumn. Secondly, spring water normally emerges at about 11 degrees centigrade throughout the year, so chalk streams tend to be warm in winter, but cool in summer when compared to

The River Hooke, a tributary of the River Frome, as it meanders through Lower Kingcombe, where the Dorset Wildlife Trust manage an extensive nature reserve.

rivers which lack a major groundwater component. Thirdly, the slow filtration of the rainwater through the chalk and the limited surface run-off explain why chalk streams emerge with crystal-clear water which is rich in major plant nutrients. Finally, because the stream is dependant upon the water level within the chalk, the source of the stream is not a fixed location. Replenishment of the aquifer in winter allows the most upstream 'winterbourne' section to flow during the winter and spring until falling water levels in the chalk eventually cause it to dry up. The stream then flows from permanent springs at what is called the 'perennial head' and life in the winterbourne must await the breaking of the springs next winter. The problems faced by plants and animals living within a winterbourne provide a stark contrast to the stable conditions within the perennial section further downstream!

The Frome has its source near Evershot, just south of Melbury Park, on the North Dorset Downs. At first it flows south and then east towards Dorchester through typical chalk country where tributaries are characteristically few in number. The Wraxall Brook and then the Hooke drain rural landscapes of great antiquity and charm before

The North Winterbourne, as it flows through the village of Winterbourne Clenston on its way to the River Stour. Sections of this intermittent stream dry out in summer as groundwater levels fall within the underlying chalk, hence the name 'winterbourne'.

The Tadnoll Brook rises on chalk but then passes through semi-natural landscape including woodland, wet heath and water meadows.

entering the upper reaches of the Frome, whilst closer to Dorchester, the Sydling Water and the Cerne flow south in sheltered valleys between steep slopes to meet the main river. Downstream of Dorchester, the South Winterbourne feeds its contribution to the Frome, drawn from land to the west and south of the county town.

The middle reaches of the Frome often occupy two or more separate channels as it journeys across the Upper Chalk before proceeding over Tertiary beds characterised by sands, gravels and clays. Because the Tadnoll Brook and the River Win both arise on the Upper Chalk their water chemistry is similar to other chalk streams, although for most of their length they flow over Tertiary Beds. However, further east, the Bovington Stream and Luckford Lake drain subcatchments which include heathland and therefore they have a higher component of surface runoff and a lower mineral content than chalk streams. As a result, high rainfall can produce a rapid increase in stream water levels and clouding of the water not only in these streams but in the Frome itself as it makes its way towards Wareham.

The Bere Stream, a tributary of the River Piddle, can be enjoyed as part of a circular walk which starts at Bere Regis.

The catchment of the Piddle, lies to the east and north of the Frome. The river rises at Alton Pancras and, like the Frome, flows south and then east in the direction of Wareham. Along this route, further tributaries including the Cheselbourne, Devil's Brook and Bere Stream drain the chalk hills to the north and supplement the flow of the main river. Nevertheless, the Piddle and some of its tributaries suffered from low flow conditions for a number of years as a result of water abstraction, but plans have now been put into place to help to resolve this issue.

The chalk streams of Dorset have received active management by man for many centuries, and their side channels, water meadow systems and associated wetlands add further interest to the landscape and increase their ecological importance. Recently, a section of the River Frome between Dorchester and Wareham, representing the most westerly example of a major chalk stream in England, has been scheduled as a Site of Special Scientific Interest (SSSI) by English Nature. To the east of Wareham the Frome and Piddle enter Poole

Water Barn Mill, East Burton, on the River Frome near Wool in the 1950s. This photograph was taken when the wheel was being used to power modern farm machinery, a reminder of the importance of water power over the centuries.

Harbour, whose rich patchwork of shoreline habitats and islands is internationally important for its wildfowl and waders.

The catchment of the River Stour is approximately twice the area of the Frome and Piddle combined, and although it extends into Somerset and Wiltshire, it is very much the Dorset Stour. Geologically the catchment can be divided into three main sections, the lower two being chalk and Tertiary beds, as in the Frome and Piddle. The source of the river is at Stourhead and the upper section, which sets the character of the main river, includes a variety of Jurassic beds which give rise to soils with a high clay content. As a consequence, the catchment upstream of Sturminster Newton has a high density of tributaries which are prone to flooding due to the rapid surface run-off. These include the Lodden, the Cale, the Lydden and its tributary, the Caundle, together with the Divelish and the Manston Brook.

The Stour then passes onto the wide belt of chalk where the density of tributaries is low once again. Between Blandford Forum and Wimborne it receives water from three tributaries, the Tarrant, the North Winterbourne and the Allen, each one with a winterbourne section and then a perennial section which flows throughout the year. The Allen is of historic importance because of its former water meadow system and although its biological interest was compromised

Two tributaries of the River Stour.
Above: The upper reaches of the River Lydden near Pulham drain a farmed landscape with pasture and woodland. After rain, the clay soils can result in turbid water and rapid increases in water level.
Below: The River Divelish at the medieval packhorse bridge at Fifehead Neville.

The River Stour at White Mill, upstream of Wimborne, showing extensive development of emergent marginal vegetation. Just visible amongst the trees on the right is a restored eighteenth century cornmill. The trees are black poplar, until recently rare and forgotten: in 1979 a line was planted further upstream on the Stour at Sturminster Newton.

in the past as a result of water abstraction, this has been addressed. At Wimborne, the river passes onto Tertiary deposits before meandering its way to Christchurch Harbour. Before this final stage, one more tributary meets the Stour.

The River Crane rises on chalk just north of Cranborne, but is renamed as the Moors River once it crosses Tertiary deposits. Despite its modest proportions, this river and its tributary, the Uddens Water, encompass both calcareous and acidic waters and support a spectacular variety of plant and animal life. As a result, much of the river has been scheduled by English Nature as an SSSI. Similar recognition has been afforded the River Avon which, though largely within Wiltshire and Hampshire, slips into Dorset as it nears its journey's end.

Both the Stour and the Avon discharge their waters into Christchurch Harbour, which is bounded to the south by Hengistbury Head and incorporates ecologically important areas, including Stanpit Marsh. In view of the high level of urbanization in this part of Dorset and the consequent pressures on water quality and recreation within the Harbour, attention is now being given to the development of a long-term strategy for sustainable use of this important resource.

There are, of course, many other streams and rivers in Dorset which help to mould the landscape. The rivers Axe and Yeo both rise in the north-west, only to leave the county as they flow to the sea. However, in the south-west, a collection of small river catchments complete their journey to the coast within Dorset. The complex geology of this area results in striking scenery and both the Char and the Brit are important components of this unspoilt landscape as they flow towards Charmouth, Bridport and the sea. A little further east, the River Bride flows in a westerly direction from near Hardy's Monument through more gentle countryside to the sea at Burton Bradstock. Continuing eastwards, several small streams pour into the Fleet and Weymouth Bay, most notably the River Wey itself, which ends its journey at

The Moors River has been scheduled as a Site of Special Scientific Interest (SSSI) because of its rich plant and animal communities. Troublefield, shown here, is also a Dorset Wildlife Trust wet grassland reserve.

Radipole Lake, an urban treat for birdwatchers.

Within Purbeck, the twin arms of the Corfe River flow through farmland on Wealden Clay resulting in a flashy river which then bursts through the Purbeck hills at Corfe Castle and over the Tertiary Beds to Poole Harbour. Further north, within the Harbour, after the Frome and Piddle have released their waters into the Wareham Channel at Swineham Point, the Sherford River meets the same channel via Lytchett Bay. It rises from springs in the chalk near Bloxworth, but for the most part it journeys through heavily wooded areas, including Wareham Forest and then on through farmland across the Tertiary Beds.

The management of our rivers to balance the varied demands we place upon them is a complex task, involving the active collaboration of many different organisations. The Environment Agency has the leading role in this process, with many specific responsibilities including water resources, pollution prevention and control, flood defence and recreation, in addition to the protection of fisheries and the conservation and enhancement of the wildlife in our rivers. English Nature has statutory duties for the promotion of nature conservation, and works in close cooperation with the Environment Agency to maintain and enhance the biological diversity and natural features of our rivers.

Dorset is particularly fortunate in having a Research Institute devoted to the study of the chemistry and biology of rivers. The River Laboratory, on the banks of the River Frome at East Stoke near Wareham, was planned as a purpose-built laboratory by the Freshwater Biological Association and built in 1963. Since then, teams of scientists with specialist knowledge of water chemistry, aquatic botany, the invertebrate fauna and fish biology have increased our knowledge and understanding of the structure and functioning of river systems in Dorset, and further afield. Much of the strategic research has been funded by the Natural Environment Research Council (NERC) but commissioned research to solve practical problems and provide new solutions is also important. Scientists at the Laboratory became part of the NERC Institute of Freshwater Ecology (IFE) in 1989 and in April 2000, they joined with colleagues from the nearby Institute of Terrestrial Ecology at Furzebrook to form the Centre for

The Corfe River downstream of Corfe Castle flows through a landscape of pastures on its way to the Wytch channel and Poole Harbour.

Ecology and Hydrology Dorset (CEH Dorset). They now occupy refurbished accommodation at the Winfrith Technology Centre, whilst retaining access to the River Laboratory facilities, and research projects continue to provide information and understanding for the sustainable management and conservation of our rivers.

PLANTS

A river-side walk in Dorset is sure to bring home the importance of plants in lowland rivers. Whereas the plant life in a mountain stream may be dominated by mosses and algae on rocks and boulders, in Dorset, many rivers have an abundance of higher plants adapted for life within, on the surface and at the margins of the river. Apart from their aesthetic appeal, plants have a major effect on the movement of water and sediments and create a variety of habitats which are used by invertebrates, fish, birds and mammals. We are all familiar with the role of plants in the food chain and the sight of a mute swan (*Cygnus olor*) eating water crowfoot (*Ranunculus penicillatus*) has much in common with a cow cropping grass. But in truth, only a small proportion of fresh weed is normally consumed by the vertebrate or invertebrate fauna. In spring and summer, submerged plants offer a large surface area for the growth of microscopic algae, which are then grazed by invertebrates. In autumn, the weed starts to decay, but it also acts as a trap for autumn-shed leaves and together these food sources sustain many invertebrates through the winter.

Fool's watercress (*left*) and wild common watercress (*right*) can be found along the margins of Dorset's winterbournes.

A spectacular sight on Dorset's chalk-streams in the spring. The white-petalled flowers of water crowfoot fill the River Frome at Frampton.

Plant communities vary with river type. Along the length of a chalk stream, for example, species composition changes from source to mouth. In the winterbourne section, fools watercress (*Apium nodiflorum*) and common watercress (*Rorippa nasturtium-aquaticum*) may occur within and at the margins of the stream, whilst water crowfoot can show spectacular growth in spring, before assuming a different growth form as the stream dries out in summer. Further downstream, where flow is permanent, water crowfoot continues to dominate unshaded sections of river, and its dark green beds produce an aerial patchwork of white-petalled flowers above the water surface in spring and early summer. Luxuriant growth of water crowfoot at this time of year can fill the channel, resulting in summer flooding of adjacent agricultural land, despite the fact that the amount of water flowing down the river is decreasing. On the Frome, between

River water dropwort produces finely divided leaves under water but eventually breaks the surface to display aerial shoots and white flowerheads in summer. The bridge in the background is White Mill, over the Stour at Sturminster Marshall.

Dorchester and Wareham, it has been normal practice for the Environment Agency to cut weed and allow it to float downstream before removing it at boom sites. Although this reduces the level of water in the river, it has the potential for impacting on fishery and other interests. Work is currently underway to evaluate the additional consequences of weed cutting. Apart from water crowfoot, other submergents are also present, including starwort (*Callitriche obtusangula*), which forms elongated light green beds in slack silted areas, and lesser water-parsnip (*Berula erecta*) which grows as a creeping carpet of weed, favouring areas where bankside trees offer partial shade across the river.

A number of rivers in Dorset, including the Frome and Piddle, are important for a submergent weed with bright green finely divided leaves, river water-dropwort (*Oenanthe fluviatilis*). This species is

Greater willowherb and meadowsweet frequently add a splash of colour to the margins of our lowland rivers

confined to north-western Europe and although it is relatively common in southern England, it deserves careful management because it is more common here than anywhere else in Europe.

Downstream, the variety of emergent and marginal plants increases. Reed sweet-grass (*Glyceria maxima*), reed canary-grass (*Phalaris arundinacea*) and branched bur-reed (*Sparganium erectum*) provide refuge from mid-stream flows for a wide range of invertebrates below the water line and resting places for adult insects above water. In addition, greater willowherb (*Epilobium hirsutum*), meadowsweet (*Filipendula ulmaria*), comfrey (*Symphytum officinale*), purple loosestrife (*Lythrum salicaria*) and many other flowers offer an ever-changing patchwork of colour along the river bank.

A characteristic feature of our chalk streams is the commercial growing of watercress. There are nine separate cress farms within the Frome and Piddle catchments and each one has its own supply of high quality groundwater. Another advantage of groundwater is that year-

The watercress beds on the Bere Stream at Doddings Farm, Bere Regis,
early in the twentieth century.
Watercress is still grown on the same beds today.

round production of watercress is possible because of the relatively
high temperature of groundwater in winter. The plants are raised from
seedlings on extensive gravel beds, and although the volume of
groundwater licensed for cress growing is substantial, most of it is
returned to the river, close to the point of abstraction.

The less predictable flow regime of the River Stour and its
tributaries presents problems for some plants in winter, but the lower
flows in summer allow rich communities of submerged, floating and
emergent plants to flourish. The clay substratum encourages the
development of the common clubrush (*Schoenoplectus lacustris*) and

Left: The arrowhead's distinctive aerial leaves and flowers are a frequent sight on shallow, slow-flowing sections of the River Stour in summer.

Right: The flowering rush occurs in shallow water in some sections of the Stour, Frome and Piddle and associated ditches.

also the yellow water-lily (*Nuphar lutea*), which produces thin leaves below the waterline plus thick floating leaves alongside its bright yellow flowers at the surface. Further variety in leaf form and flower can be found amongst stands of arrowhead (*Sagittaria sagittifolia*)

Spikes of purple loosestrife are frequent in midsummer on some streams, ditches and water meadows but are rarely found on chalk.

Alders are frequently encountered along river banks in Dorset, as here on
the River Hooke at Kingcombe. Their autumn-shed leaves are eaten by
stream invertebrates, whilst siskins and other small birds seek food in their
upper branches in winter.

Although the Loddon pondweed is confined to a handful of rivers in England, it is frequent in the middle reaches of the River Stour.

with its white flowers and in the attractive pink of the flowering rush (*Butomus umbellatus*).

The Moors River below the Uddens confluence is a nationally recognised example of a small yet species-rich watercourse, but the Stour itself has its own treasures. Apart from its rich plant communities it also plays host to some rare aquatic plants. The Loddon pondweed (*Potamogeton nodosus*) is one such species. It grows in gravelly reaches between Child Okeford and Blandford on the Stour, but is otherwise confined to the Bristol Avon, the Thames and its tributary the Loddon. The native sub-species of the summer snowflake (*Leucojum aestivum*) is also rare, but may be found between Blandford and Wimborne on the river bank and on islands within the river.

Finally, in addition to instream and riverbank vegetation, the presence of bankside trees can have important consequences for our streams and rivers. On small streams, heavy shading by trees can limit the growth of submerged plants and marginal vegetation, whilst providing an alternative form of food for many stream invertebrates in the form of autumn-shed leaves. Alder trees are very characteristic of many river banks where they provide bank stability but also a refuge for both fish and invertebrates amongst their underwater root systems. In recent years, a fungal disease (*Phytophthora*) has been affecting some alders across much of England and Wales. Fortunately, it appears that some trees are resistant. Nevertheless, the importance of alders is such that any major loss would have a substantial effect on both the riverside landscape and its ecology.

INVERTEBRATES

With practice, most naturalists can identify marginal aquatic plants, although some of the submerged species can be problematic! In contrast, the huge variety of invertebrates in running waters can be a barrier to those with an interest in naming the major types. This is unfortunate, because some knowledge of the variety and adaptations of invertebrates, together with a basic understanding of their role in the ecosystem, brings its own reward.

In Dorset, many streams and rivers support a variety of non-insects, including flatworms (Tricladida), snails (Gastropoda), mussels (Bivalvia), true worms (Oligochaeta), leeches (Hirudinea) and crustaceans (Malacostraca), together with a somewhat wider range of insects. These may include representatives from most but not necessarily all of the major groups, including mayflies (Ephemeroptera), stoneflies (Plecoptera), dragonflies and damselflies (Odonata), bugs (Hemiptera), beetles (Coleoptera), alderflies

Caddis larvae often have filamentous gills on the abdominal segments and always possess a pair of hooks on the last segment. *Hydropsyche*, shown here, constructs a silken net in which it captures small animals and other particles of food.

The freshwater shrimp is abundant in many streams and rivers in Dorset. It plays a vital role in the breakdown of organic matter (e.g. tree leaves), but often falls prey to predatory invertebrates and fish.

(Megaloptera), caddis (Trichoptera) and true flies (Diptera). Overall, there are several hundred species of invertebrates in the streams and rivers of Dorset.

The fauna at a particular site is largely determined by the environmental conditions, and therefore the type of river and the location of the site along the watercourse are important in determining the invertebrate community. However, pollution and other forms of environmental stress can also affect species composition, and the sensitivity of different members of the invertebrate fauna to stress is now widely used in the biological monitoring of river quality.

Many high quality sites in the middle reaches of rivers in Dorset include over one hundred species of invertebrates, with life cycles ranging from a few weeks to two years or more. One way through this confusing variety is to allocate species to 'functional feeding groups' in an attempt to understand their role in the scheme of things. For example, the freshwater shrimp (*Gammarus pulex*), which can occur at very high densities in chalk streams is a 'shredder', performing an essential role in breaking down and consuming autumn-shed leaves. In this way it makes small particles available to other invertebrates and by converting coarse organic material into its own body tissue, it provides an important source of food for fish, including the bullhead (*Cottus gobio*), the grayling (*Thymallus thymallus*) and brown trout (*Salmo trutta*). Algae, which use both gravel and submerged leaves as a surface for attachment, are cropped by 'grazer-scrapers', including snails and caddis with a preference for hard surfaces, and some mayfly nymphs and non-biting midge larvae (Chironomidae) which feed in large numbers on plant surfaces.

The progressive breakdown by invertebrates of tree leaves, water weeds and algal material results in the production of fine particles within the water column and on the river bed. The so-called 'collector-filterers', most notably blackfly larvae (Simuliidae) passively filter the water for fine suspended material using their impressive head fans, whilst on the river bed the 'collector-gatherers', including the true worms (Oligochaeta), consume fine material in a further recycling process. In addition to these four main feeding groups there are also invertebrate predators. Of the non-insects, each individual species of flatworm and leech has its own preferred prey organism, whilst the insect predators exhibit a range of different feeding mechanisms and behaviour patterns which ensure the success of the immature stages of dragonflies, alderflies, and some caddis and true flies.

Mayfly larvae in the genus *Baetis* are torpedo-shaped to withstand high current velocities. Within weed beds they graze on surface algae and particles of detritus.

The native white-clawed crayfish has a restricted distribution in Dorset as a result of crayfish plague, a fungal infection carried by an introduced species, the signal crayfish.

A good example of a predator is one of our largest and most spectacular native invertebrates, the white-clawed crayfish. This species, which can live for more than ten years, is a predator on many invertebrates and small fish, but will also eat macrophytes, algae and decaying tree leaves. Thus, the varied members of the invertebrate community perform an essential role in the functioning of the river system by processing a wide range of food resources and making them available to the next trophic level, predominantly the fish.

The unique features of winterbournes and the problems faced by invertebrates attempting to colonize them are particularly relevant to Dorset. For example, a survey of the South Winterbourne stream, a tributary of the River Frome led to the discovery of a blackfly (*Metacnephia amphora*) new to science in the early 1970s. The larvae grow through the early spring when the stream is flowing and pupate and emerge as adults within two months, thus avoiding the drying of the stream in summer. Although this species has now been found at a small number of sites, including several winterbourne streams in the chalk belt of the Stour catchment, it remains rare. A similar strategy of spring growth and emergence is adopted by a species of mayfly

(*Paraleptophlebia werneri*), whose eggs remain in the dry stream bed until the return of flow the following winter.

More recent studies on a variety of headwater streams within the Stour catchment, and elsewhere in Dorset, have revealed that other rare and vulnerable species are characteristic of and frequently confined to headwater streams. The need for awareness and sympathetic land and water management to ensure that these vulnerable streams are safeguarded is now a priority.

Within the middle and lower reaches of the Frome and Piddle, we find rich invertebrate communities with a wide variety of mayflies, caddis and true flies. The predictable flow regime and year-round availability of a range of different habitats and food resources enable these rivers to support high densities of non-insects and insects. Chalk streams have long been recognised for the richness and abundance of their communities, but it is now apparent that parts of the Stour and some of its tributaries are also species-rich. A study of the Moors River and Uddens Water by scientists from the River Laboratory yielded 322 taxa, and regular monitoring by the Environment Agency is providing evidence that the lower Stour is also exceptionally rich. A number of

The rare mayfly, *Paraleptophlebia werneri*, is adapted to the intermittent flow regime of a winterbourne. The larva completes its growth and emerges before the stream dries. Eggs laid by the adult survive in the dry stream-bed and then hatch when water returns.

A pair of scarce chaser dragonflies mating. The male, in front, clasps the female on the back of her head. She then collects sperm from an accessory organ on the underside of the male's abdomen.

rarities occur at some of these sites, most notably the scarce chaser dragonfly (*Libellula fulva*). Dorset is an important location for this species and after emergence in late May, adults may be found in the lower Frome, Stour (including the Moors River) and the lower Avon

Some mention must also be made of the notorious 'Blandford Fly' (*Simulium posticatum*), which can inflict painful bites on humans. Detective work and ingenuity by scientists from the River Laboratory revealed critical features in the life cycle of this blackfly, and the means to control it. The Blandford Fly has only one annual generation and in July the females take a blood meal from a mammal, typically believed

Damselflies have slender bodies and unlike dragonflies, are weak fliers incapable of hovering. The white-legged damselfly is typical of larger river systems such as the Dorset Stour.

In summer, the River Stour at Blandford supports a varied mixture of marginal vegetation (marsh woundwort and meadowsweet) and instream vegetation including yellow water lily. Fortunately, the once notorious 'Blandford fly' is now being brought under control.

to be a horse or cow, but sometimes a human! This meal provides nourishment for the development of the eggs which are then deposited in the dry vertical banks of the River Stour. There the eggs remain until late winter, when rising water levels normally wash them into the river. The larvae then hatch, attach to water plants and start to filter feed on the planktonic algae which are abundant in the River Stour each spring. Once growth is complete, they pupate on the weed before emerging as adults in late May and June. After a detailed evaluation, this insect is now being controlled in an environmentally friendly and carefully targeted manner by spraying the larval habitat each spring with a bacterium which is then filtered from the water by the larvae.

The fisherman's mayfly (*Ephemera danica*) emerges in late May and must escape the attention of birds in order to mate and return to water to lay its eggs.

Once in the gut, a toxin within the bacterium is activated which is fatal to the blackfly larvae. The success of this annual treatment is now clearly apparent, with the number of bites reported by local doctors falling from over 1,000 per year in the late 1980s to under 50 in recent years.

Most aquatic insects leave the water to complete their life cycle, and this is when they are most easily seen. One of the larger insects to emerge in late April is a caddisfly, the Grannom, (*Brachycentrus subnubilus*) which bursts from its pupal case on water crowfoot, rises to the surface and flies off. It then has to feed and mate before laying a green mass of gelatinous eggs below the waterline. In time the larvae hatch, feed and grow by filtering small particles from the water and eventually pupate on water crowfoot the following spring. The streams and rivers of Dorset support many different species of caddis flies but, for the naturalist and fisherman, the different species of mayflies are more eye-catching.

Mayflies are unique in that 'subimagos' emerge from the water and fly off but then cast a further skin to produce the full adult or 'imago'. In late May, the fisherman's mayfly (*Ephemera danica*) having spent two years as a nymph, feeding on small particles within its burrow, risks all as it rises to the water surface and attempts to fly off before

Demoiselles are our largest and most spectacular damselflies. The beautiful demoiselle (*top*) is characteristic of gravelly fast-flowing streams, whereas the banded demoiselle (*below*) occurs further downstream. The predatory larvae live amongst vegetation and normally take two years to develop before emerging in late May.

being snapped up by vigilant trout. The adults, like all mayflies, do not feed, but after mating the larger females deposit several thousand eggs on the water surface. The eggs then sink to the bottom and stick to the substratum before hatching. Some species of mayflies have a one-year life cycle but several of the species mimicked by dry fly fishermen have two or more generations per year and form an important source of food for trout. In order to maintain their preferred location along a river system, some species of mayflies fly upstream before depositing their eggs, thus counteracting the tendency for the larval stages to drift downstream.

Each group of insects has its own particular strategy for survival. Whereas the eggs of alderflies are deposited on marginal vegetation to enable the hatching larvae to fall into the water, many of the more familiar dragonflies and damselflies carefully deposit individual eggs on or even within the tissues of submerged water plants. A short section of river may hold dozens of species of non-biting midges and because the larvae are often very abundant, they can emerge in such numbers that their dancing swarms can sometimes look like columns of smoke. They supply a snack to many dragonflies and birds alike, yet still survive in numbers to deposit their egg masses and repopulate the river once more with larvae which then form an essential item of food for the other freshwater invertebrates and fish.

Given the huge variety of invertebrates to be found in our streams and rivers, it is not surprising that they exploit a wide range of habitats in their quest to maintain station, find food and avoid predators. Some live on the surface of the river gravel, whilst others occur within the substratum, sometimes at considerable depths and even extending laterally beyond the river bank itself. Many invertebrates are found at their highest densities on submerged water weed or in marginal vegetation where the opportunities for selecting different current speeds and food resources are considerable.

Not all habitats are available for colonisation throughout the year. In particular, many submerged water weeds grow through the spring and summer, only to die back or be ripped out by high winter flows. Although most marginal vegetation also dies back in winter, the submerged roots and stems remain an important refuge for some invertebrates, enabling them to avoid high current speeds in mid-river.

Left: Alderfly larvae have lateral filamentous gills and large mandibles for seizing their food, which includes freshwater worms and fly larvae.

Right: Adult alderflies have dark glossy wings held over the abdomen and can be seen on bankside vegetation in early summer. The female lays a rectangular block of several hundred eggs on vegetation overhanging the water.

The following spring, some of the invertebrates which over-wintered in the margins move on to new growth of submerged vegetation whilst many insects which over-wintered in the egg stage also colonise this fast developing habitat with its surface algae.

As our understanding of this complex ecosystem develops, it becomes clear that man's activities in the form of weed-cutting, dredging and the management of marginal vegetation and bankside trees can all have important consequences for the invertebrates which play a vital role in the functioning of our rivers. The increasing frequency of droughts and flood events observed over the last fifteen years has also served to demonstrate the importance of events outside of our immediate control. Under drought conditions, the growth of water crowfoot is usually poor, resulting in reduced habitat and food for some mayfly larvae such as *Baetis* and blackfly larvae (*Simulium*) which would normally occur in high densities in weed beds. Fortunately, there is evidence to suggest that in streams of high biological quality, the return of normal or high flows encourages the regrowth of water crowfoot, accompanied by its characteristic invertebrate assemblages.

FISH

For many people, fish symbolise the fascination of rivers, and they have long been used by man as a yardstick for river health. After all, fish place many exacting demands on a river if they are to find suitable spawning locations, nursery areas for the early stages, and both habitat and food to sustain them through the changing seasons.

In Britain as a whole, there are less than 60 species of freshwater fish, but in Dorset over 30 species are known from the freshwater and

This three sea-winter salmon was caught by Dr Mike Ladle on the River Frome at East Stoke in the 1970s. It weighted 26½ lbs (12 kg).

On the River Frome at East Stoke scientists use an acoustic bubble screen to divert migrating salmon smolts into the Mill Stream (bottom left) where they can be counted automatically without being handled.

tidal reaches of our rivers. In fact, the River Avon is thought to have more species than any other British river. The Stour also has a rich community of salmonids and coarse fish. In contrast, the Frome and Piddle have fewer coarse fish species but their salmonids are recognized as a very important resource. Each one of these rivers plays host to both the Atlantic salmon (*Salmo salar*) and migratory sea-trout (*Salmo trutta*) as they return to freshwater from the sea. The sustainable management of these fish is an important issue for the Environment Agency, research workers and fishermen alike.

The Atlantic salmon in particular has a special fascination for fishermen and naturalists. Sadly, the general concern over declining salmon stocks applies to southern chalk streams, as elsewhere. Scientists at the River Laboratory in Dorset have been monitoring the salmon runs on the Frome for over 25 years and this represents the longest and most comprehensive study for any English river. Records from the Frome fish counter indicate that the number of returning adults has dropped from just under 4,000 adults in 1973 to just under 1,200 adults in 1997. It is now thought that the main problem is likely

The bullhead, a well camouflaged bottom feeder, occupies an important role within small chalk streams. Spawning occurs in early spring and the yellow eggs are laid in batches on the underside of stones.

to be in the marine phase of the life history but, nevertheless, there are additional factors which are known to affect the freshwater phase. Long-term rod catches of salmon within the river and commercial fishing in the estuary both show declines, although the numbers taken are a variable proportion of the total salmon run. Fish that have spent three winters in the sea enter the lower reaches of the river in March and April, followed by two sea-winter fish in May-June and one-sea-winter fish (grilse) in June-July. All the fish then move upstream to the main river spawning grounds in autumn, often when river flows have started to increase. The decline in the number of three sea-winter fish which average around 10kg in weight is of great concern, as is the fact that the mean length of grilse has also declined. Careful management and monitoring of salmon spawning habitat coupled with improvement of nursery habitat is now a priority to ensure that adequate numbers of salmon smolts make their way back down to the sea. But how can the success of this operation be determined? An innovative technique developed by River Laboratory staff for counting these delicate fish automatically without the need to capture them is now providing another essential element in the quest to understand and reverse the decline of the salmon.

The radio-tagging of pike on the River Frome has lead to major advances in our understanding of the biology of this impressive predator.

In addition to salmon and migratory trout, which favour the middle and lower reaches of the major chalk streams, the upper reaches of the Frome and the middle reaches of the Piddle also support good populations of brown trout. Further downstream on the Frome, below Dorchester, the grayling is an important member of the fish community, but curiously, this species is absent from the Piddle. Although the upper sections of the chalk streams and their tributaries are generally regarded as trout streams, smaller fish including bullhead, minnow (*Phoxinus phoxinus*) and stone loach (*Noemacheilus barbatulus*) are normally common and play a more significant role in the functioning of the river system. The bullhead, for example, has been shown to contribute over 80% of total fish production in some small streams.

Further downstream, coarse fish become more abundant, and fast-growing pike (*Esox lucius*) have ample opportunity to prey on species such as minnow and dace. In a new study by CEH Dorset scientists, individual pike have been radio-tagged to gain a greater understanding of how they find their food, avoid winter floods and ensure successful breeding. It is now becoming clear that, for most of the year, pike occupy distinct home ranges which may be several

The river lamprey is not regarded as a true fish because it lacks proper jaws. However, it uses sharp teeth within its circular mouth to attach itself to fish.

hundred metres of river in length. They can move through the full length of their home range in a single day and this suggests that they have a much more active hunting strategy than was previously suspected. In winter, during high river flows, they have been detected in nearby flooded fields and ditches, whilst in spring, larger scale movements of several kilometres have been observed, probably related to their spawning behaviour.

Within the tidal reaches of the Frome and Piddle, several marine species also occur, including bass (*Dicentrarchus labrax*), thick-lipped mullet (*Crenimugil labrosus*), thin-lipped mullet (*Chelon ramada*) and flounder (*Platichthys flesus*). On the Frome, these last two species have been found several kilometres upstream near East Stoke.

Apart from salmon and migratory trout, a number of other fish move into our rivers from the marine environment to breed. These include the impressive sea lamprey (*Petromyzon marinus*) and the smaller river lamprey (*Lampetra fluviatilis*) neither of which are true fish since they lack proper jaws. They both occur in the Frome, Piddle, Stour and Avon, as does a third species, the diminutive brook lamprey (*Lampetra planeri*) which remains in freshwater throughout its life and spawns on well-aerated river gravels. The smelt (*Osmerus eperlanus*), is a small migratory species, noted for its characteristic

The River Stour's reputation as a coarse fishery owes much its populations of barbel (*top*) and roach *(bottom)*.
The barbel, a characteristic species of the lower Stour, has two pairs of barbels on the head which it uses to detect invertebrate prey on the riverbed.
The roach is a common species in Dorset, and grows at an exceptional rate in both the rivers Stour and Frome. It feeds on invertebrates and some plants and lays its eggs on waterweeds.

cucumber-like smell. Within Dorset, it has only been recorded in the lower Frome and, as yet, little is known of its detailed life history.

The River Stour is recognised as a fine coarse fishery, but salmonids are also common in the lower reaches of the main river and in some of the tributaries. Most of the salmon and migratory trout which move through Christchurch harbour enter the River Avon, but salmon do spawn in the Stour itself below Blandford, although the rod catch has been negligible for some years. The lower reaches of the Tarrant and the Allen are also used for spawning whilst migratory trout use the main river plus the River Crane and Mannington Brook in the Moors subcatchment. Brown trout occur in the lower reaches of the main river and its tributaries with the highest densities in the chalk tributaries, including the Crane and Allen. Unfortunately, the Allen suffered from low flows for a number of years as a consequence of groundwater abstraction which, in turn, reduced the spawning and nursery habitat for salmonids. However, reductions in the abstraction licence were agreed and have now been implemented by the water company.

A wide variety of coarse fish dominate the full length of the River Stour and include bleak (*Alburnus alburnus*), chub (*Leuciscus cephalus*) and barbel (*Barbus barbus*), which are absent from the Frome and Piddle. Roach (*Rutilus rutilus*) are common throughout the river, and are prized by fishermen. Studies have demonstrated that in the Stour, and also in the nearby Frome, the roach grow faster than those in most other European rivers. Downstream of Wimborne the river is renowned for its population of barbel.

Finally the Stour, together with the major chalk streams in Dorset, still supports populations of eels (*Anguilla anguilla*) after they have completed their incredible journey from their breeding grounds in the Sargasso Sea, aided by the Gulf stream. However, the numbers of immature eels, sometimes known as glass eels, reaching the coastline of Europe have been declining for many years. As a consequence, numbers of the more mature pigmented elvers have also declined. This problem is now receiving attention because eels form a significant part of the food chain, being taken by a variety of birds and also by otters.

BIRDS

Dorset plays host to a wide variety of birds. Rivers and their adjacent wetlands provide suitable conditions for a number of different species in the breeding season, on passage and through the winter. During the nesting season, vertical river banks, bankside vegetation and man-made structures such as bridges are all used as nest sites because they offer close proximity to a ready supply of food.

The dipper (*Cinclus cinclus*), is a very uncommon breeding resident in Dorset, because its specialist requirements are only met in the fast upland streams in the west of the county. Here it feeds underwater in shallow riffles, taking a variety of invertebrates, but with a particular preference for caddis larvae. Dippers pair and hold territory throughout the winter and start breeding early, sometimes rearing as many as three broods in well concealed nests built in natural or man-made crevices close to the water.

The dipper occurs infrequently on some of our fast upland watercourses in the west of the county, such as the rivers Axe, Brit and Hooke.

The grey wagtail has a high-pitched two-syllable call easily heard above the sound of flowing water. This male has caught a damselfly.

Less specialised than the dipper and far more widespread in Dorset is the grey wagtail (*Motacilla cinerea*), a resident species whose name describes the colour of its back but fails to mention the black throat and bright yellow underparts which make the male bird so elegant in summer. Look for this long-tailed species near bridges, where its lively search for insects associated with fast-flowing rivers and streams adds interest to any riverside walk.

However, it is the kingfisher (*Alcedo atthis*) that leaves the strongest impression as we are alerted by that sudden high pitched call and turquoise flash of colour as it speeds torpedo-like along the watercourse. Kingfishers prefer the lowland rivers of central and eastern Dorset, and although they breed on our chalk streams, the Dorset Stour with its well-developed vertical earth banks provides optimal conditions for nesting and an abundant supply of small fish through the summer and autumn.

The Dorset Stour provides kingfishers with earth banks in which they excavate their nest tunnel and a plentiful supply of minnows during the breeding season.

A little grebe in full breeding plumage feeding a chick.

Where Dorset's major rivers and their tributaries have stands of bankside vegetation, a number of familiar water birds including the mute swan, moorhen (*Gallinula chloropus*), coot (*Fulica atra*) and little grebe (*Tachybaptus ruficollis*) nest in the margins. Although breeding adults eat a variety of submerged and emergent vegetation, newly hatched young add a high protein supplement to their diet in the form of a wide range of invertebrates.

In spring and summer, well developed areas of marginal vegetation frequently play host to the ubiquitous sedge warbler (*Acrocephalus schoenobaenus*) whilst the reed warbler (*Acrocephalus scirpaceus*) is indeed the most characteristic warbler of the common reed (*Phragmites australis*). It takes patience to distinguish the varied and energetic song of the sedge warbler from the more measured and repetitious strains of the reed warbler. In contrast, the cetti's warbler (*Cettia cetti*), has an unmistakable explosive song, which includes an insistent phrase somewhat reminiscent of its name. This resident species was first confirmed as a British breeding bird as recently as 1972, but can now be heard, and less frequently seen, at Radipole Lake and at a number of downstream locations on rivers which drain into Poole and Christchurch Harbours: the riverside walk along the

In summer sedge warblers *(top)* can be found at many riverside locations but reed warblers *(bottom)* are restricted to reedbeds.

The northern lapwing is a common winter visitor to the lower
reaches of our major river systems, but has been in serious
decline as a breeding species.

River Frome downstream of Wareham is one favoured location.

The wetlands associated with Dorset's major rivers are dependant
upon the maintenance of high water levels in spring and early summer
if they are to be suitable as breeding areas for waders such as redshank

The banded demoiselle is found at high densities along many of our well-
vegetated rivers and is sometimes taken by insect-eating birds.

Although Poole Harbour is an important wintering area for waders
such as the redshank, few remain to breed in our river valleys
and around the Harbour.

(*Tringa totanus*) and northern lapwing (*Vanellus vanellus*). At present,
both these waders are in serious decline as breeding species. However,
water level management plans are now under development for a
number of trial areas in the lower Frome and Piddle valleys and
further schemes for raising water levels in selected areas within the
Stour catchment are also proposed. In time, all these schemes should
be of long-term benefit to a number of our wetland birds.

Many other birds and in particular those which rely on insects as a
source of food are frequent visitors to our rivers, where swarms of
mayflies, caddisflies and true flies provide an easy feast. They include
such summer migrants as sand martins (*Riparia riparia*), house
martins (*Delichon urbica*) and barn swallows (*Hirundo rustica*). The
hobby (*Falco subbuteo*), an attractive falcon capable of taking
martins, swallows and even swifts (*Apus apus*) in flight, will also prey
on dragonflies and damselflies, such as the distinctive banded
demoiselle (*Calopteryx splendens*), before discarding their
characteristic wings along the banks of some of our lowland rivers.

During spring and autumn passage, many different birds use rivers and adjacent wetlands for feeding and resting before their onward journey. In winter, the lower sections of the major river valleys become important wintering grounds for a variety of waders and waterfowl. One of the more remarkable visitors to arrive is the Tundra swan (*Cygnus columbianus*), which can sometimes be located in small numbers in the Lower Frome and Avon valleys after its long autumn retreat from the breeding grounds in Arctic Russia. Winter can also produce the occasional surprise such as an overwintering green sandpiper (*Tringa ochropus*) at a watercress bed, or the elegant fish-eating goosander (*Mergus merganser*) on the R. Stour. In winter, little egrets (*Egretta garzetta*) from the breeding colony on Brownsea Island disperse beyond the confines of Poole Harbour and individuals may be found in all our major river valleys, stalking their prey in shallow water.

MAMMALS

Three native mammals, the water shrew (*Neomys fodiens*), the water vole (*Arvicola terrestris*) and the European otter (*Lutra lutra*) occur on rivers in Dorset. The water shrew is a small but voracious predator on a wide range of invertebrates, amphibians and fish. It occurs in association with a variety of unpolluted streams and ponds with good cover. The maximum lifespan is about 18 months and each day its food consumption exceeds its own body weight, so a reliable source of food is a necessity. In practice, records of the water shrew on rivers in Dorset are few and therefore its true status is difficult to assess, but it has been recorded at several watercress beds on chalk streams.

The water vole, alias 'Ratty' from *The Wind in the Willows*, feeds on a very wide range of grasses and bankside vegetation on rivers, ponds and drainage ditches. Surrounded by food and with a rodent's

The water vole has thick brown fur, and can be distinguished from the brown rat by its smaller ears, shorter muzzle and a shorter lightly haired tail.

Midwinter morning light on the River Frome at Wool.
The river supports an important population of water voles.

ability to perpetuate its species, it used to be common on rivers throughout most of lowland Britain. However, the familiar sight of a vole sitting on its haunches and using its front paws to cram food into its mouth or paddling furiously to reach bankside safety has now become much less frequent in many parts of the country. Although the water vole has suffered a long-term decline over the past century, this has developed into a population crash, and it is now Britain's fastest declining mammal. The reasons for this decline are many, but include habitat loss and fragmentation, pollution, bank protection works and predation by an introduced species, the mink, which can hunt water voles on land, in water and also in their burrows. Two national surveys in 1989-90 and 1996-98 recorded a reduction in the population of 88%. In consequence, the water vole is now a priority species in the UK Biodiversity Action Plan, and the Environment Agency has the leading role in coordinating the various actions required to reverse this trend.

Within Dorset, water vole surveys are undertaken by a network of volunteers coordinated by the Dorset Wildlife Trust's Rivers and Wetland Project. The results from the first county survey, which took place in 1996-97, were compared with historical records and indicated a less dramatic decline than the national trend. The 2001-02 survey has provided some encouraging increases in the number of positive records throughout Dorset, including the Char and Bride in west Dorset where no evidence of water voles was found in 1996-97. The middle reaches of the Frome, in particular, are now recognized as a core area for water voles in England as well as in Dorset and management plans are being drawn up to conserve these populations.

The third native species, the otter, is also a UK Biodiversity Action Plan species and in this case the Environment Agency and the Wildlife Trusts are lead partners in a programme to maintain and expand the existing populations in England and Wales. The otter is an impressive carnivore which feeds on fish, amphibians and crustaceans. Adult males can be up to 1.5 metres in length, over 10 kg in weight and consume 1 kg of food each day. The severe reduction in otter populations in the late 1950s and 1960s, primarily as a result of pesticides but also due to loss of suitable habitat, is well known. However, as a result of improvements in water quality and positive

Otters have recently recolonised many of Dorset's rivers. Volunteers in the Dorset Otter Group have documented this process by searching for signs such as spraint and tracks.

efforts to improve bankside habitat, including the construction of artificial holts, the decline has been reversed and in some areas of Wales and south-west England, otter numbers may now be close to their breeding capacity.

The Dorset Otter Group, supported by Dorset Wildlife Trust, has a wide network of volunteers who look for spraint and otter tracks in order to document the recolonisation of rivers in Dorset by otters. With each year, the flow of records provides an increasingly optimistic picture of the return of the otter to the Stour, Frome, Piddle and, more recently, to the rivers of west Dorset, including the Yeo, Axe, Char, Brit and Bride. Inevitably, there are setbacks and road deaths at bridge sites take their toll, as did a fyke net set for eels on the Stour which led to the drowning of a female otter and two cubs in 2002. Nevertheless, the long-term commitment of several statutory organizations working in partnership, together with the activities of the Dorset Otter Group in recording otters and building artificial holts, is leading to encouraging results.

A further activity of the Dorset Otter Group is the construction
of artificial otter holts. This partially constructed holt will
be covered with branches and brushwood and allowed to become
overgrown with brambles.

The North American mink is well established as a breeding species and although it has a varied diet, its ability to catch water voles has contributed to their drastic decline.

All the information on the distribution of otters (and water voles) is sent to the Dorset Environmental Records Centre (DERC) who assemble the records and produce current distribution maps. DERC was established in 1976 as an independent organization to collate information on all of Dorset's wildlife, and it performs a unique role in the collation and dissemination of important information on the flora and fauna of the county.

The mink (*Mustela vison*), a native of North America, escaped from British fur farms earlier this century and was first reported breeding in the wild in Devon in 1956. It is now widespread throughout Britain, including Dorset, but is rarely seen except by those who spend long hours on the river bank. It has more catholic tastes than the otter and takes fish, birds and mammals, including water voles. Our rivers also provide food for bats in the form of flying insects. Thus, pipistrelles (*Pipistrellus pipistrellus*) and Daubenton's bats (*Myotis daubentoni*) take over as swallows and martins complete their day shift and go to roost.

THE MANAGEMENT OF RIVERS IN DORSET

Dorset is essentially a rural county with no big cities or centres of heavy industrialisation and it enjoys the benefit of high quality rivers with an impressive variety of wildlife. Nevertheless, the present state of our rivers has only been achieved through the concerted action and co-operation of many organisations over a long period, and much remains to be done. Man's impact on rivers is through management of the land within the catchment, and more directly through manipulation of the quality and quantity of the water in the river, the river habitats and its wildlife.

The lower Moors river has long been recognized for its dragonflies and water plants, and many organisations have coordinated their efforts to maintain its status.

The orange-spotted emerald dragonfly is thought to be extinct in Britain, the last documented record being from the lower Moors River in 1963.

Within the county, farmers have made significant improvements in recent years in conserving soil and limiting run-off by fertilisers and farm wastes – neglect of which can easily result in siltation, enrichment and pollution of watercourses. Even so, there is a need for constant vigilance and advice on new procedures for minimising impacts, such as the adoption of buffer strips along the margins of streams and rivers. Forestry, mineral extraction and urban development take further substantial areas of land and an example of the impact of urbanisation on a river system can be found in the Moors River.

The lower Moors River was first notified as a Site of Special Scientific Interest in 1959 because of the exceptional richness of its dragonfly fauna and water plants. One dragonfly in particular, the orange-spotted emerald (*Oxygastra curtisii*), held pride of place, this part of Dorset being where it was first discovered and described in 1820. By the 1950s, the Moors River was the sole location for this species in Britain and excessive shading by bankside trees was reducing the amount of suitable habitat for the territorial males. Sadly, the final loss of this species in Britain is believed to be the result of accidental pollution caused by the Palmersford Sewage Treatment

The biological quality of a site is determined by collecting river invertebrates using a standard sampling method and comparing them with the fauna expected in the absence of pollution. The expected fauna for running water sites throughout the United Kingdom is determined using a sophisticated computer programme.

Works (STW), serving newly constructed housing estates. The last record for the orange-spotted emerald was in July 1963. Since then, housing development within the catchment has continued and strenuous efforts have been made to control run-off from the urban environment and from industrial estates. Finally, in 1992, effluent from the Palmersford STW, now operated by Wessex Water Services, was diverted by pipeline to the River Stour, since when the water quality in the Moors River has improved.

Throughout England and Wales the Environment Agency plays a crucial role in the development of a sustainable environment. The Agency has very wide-ranging responsibilities including the management of our water resources, freshwater fisheries, integrated river-basin management and the enhancement of biodiversity, together with conservation of the land, waste management, regulation of major industries, improvement of air quality and issues relating to climate change. These important topics are addressed through a series of catchment-based Local Environment Agency Plans (LEAPs). In order to achieve improvements to our local environment the Environment Agency has developed an active partnership with

An unshaded section of the River Frome near Dorchester where luxuriant growth of water crowfoot has filled the channel. Further downstream weed is sometimes cut to prevent summer flooding of adjacent land.

regional and local planning authorities, the water companies, farmers and landowners, businesses and a wide range of non-governmental organizations with an interest in the future of the countryside and its wildlife.

The chemical and biological quality of rivers in Dorset is monitored on a regular basis by the Environment Agency and assessed for compliance against stated targets. Scientists at the River Laboratory were responsible for developing a novel approach for assessing the biological quality of rivers, based on the invertebrate fauna, and since 1990 this has been the standard system for determining the biological quality of rivers throughout the United Kingdom. A similar approach is now used throughout Australia and it has also generated interest in Canada, the USA and several European countries.

To fulfill its obligations with regard to water quality, the Environment Agency takes account of a series of separate EU Directives. However, by December 2003, a new EU Directive known as the Water Framework Directive will become national legislation. This provides an overall framework for protection and action, rationalizing and updating existing water legislation to produce an integrated approach to water management in Europe. The Environment Agency will have the lead role in implementing this comprehensive legislation which includes the protection of drinking water sources, bathing and recreational waters and the protection of aquatic ecosystems.

In Dorset, the increasing demand for water for domestic, agricultural and other uses is met through a combination of groundwater and surface water sources. Heavy utilization of the groundwater resources available within the chalk belt may alter flow regimes in winterbournes and perennial chalk streams, whilst removal of water from the lower reaches of rivers reduces the flow available for dilution of effluents. Hence, difficult decisions have to be made. It was groundwater abstraction from the River Allen to satisfy the Bournemouth and Poole conurbation with its peak demand during the holiday season that resulted in low summer flows and a number of biological consequences including poor growth of weed, and the reduction of spawning and nursery habitat for salmonids. The upper and middle reaches of the River Piddle have also been affected by

The upper reaches of the River Allen looking north towards Wimborne St Giles. Agreed cuts in groundwater abstraction from the Allen at Stanbridge Mill should benefit the plants and animals along this attractive river.

groundwater abstractions over a number of years. The Environment Agency is now required to develop Catchment Abstraction Management Strategies (CAMS) for these and other rivers in Dorset. The motivation behind CAMS is to meet the reasonable needs of abstractors, while leaving enough water to conserve the aquatic ecosystem.

If we are to enjoy the flora and fauna associated with our local rivers, then the quality of water together with the amount and seasonal distribution of that water must be safeguarded. Even so, additional factors can contribute to the local or even the global extinction of species such as habitat loss and degradation, the spread of non-native species or the over-exploitation of native species. A substantial body of national and international legislation has been developed for the protection of threatened species and habitats, but this is beyond the scope of the present book. Nevertheless, one important development from the Convention on Biodiversity drawn up in Rio de Janeiro in June 1992 deserves mention. This led to the government publishing the UK Biodiversity Action Plan, followed by further reports detailing a major programme on the conservation of

River Habitat Survey procedures have been used on rivers throughout the UK to assess the physical character and quality of river habitats.

biodiversity within the UK. Lists of 'priority' Biodiversity Action Plan (BAP) species and habitats have been drawn up at the national level but actions require partnership and coordination all the way from national to local level. Within Dorset, BAP habitats (e.g. chalk rivers) and a number of BAP species associated with flowing waters (e.g. otter, water vole, southern damselfly, white-clawed crayfish) are now the subject of detailed Action Plans designed to record current distribution, identify major threats and undertake actions to promote the recovery of each species.

The importance of suitable habitat for each species has been illustrated already. Fortunately, procedures for systematically recording habitat features have now been standardized by the Environment Agency, with specialist input from a number of organizations, including staff from the River Laboratory. River Habitat Survey (RHS) is a method for assessing the physical character and quality of river habitats. The protocol has already been applied at many thousands of sites throughout the UK and has confirmed that many lowland rivers have modified channels resulting in habitat degradation and loss of associated wetlands. These results are now being used to conserve and restore wildlife habitats within and alongside rivers in order to enhance biodiversity. As evidence accumulates, it is now becoming clear that rivers and their wildlife do have great potential for recovery if management is based on understanding.

The introduction of non-native species poses a different set of problems, some of which may be irreversible. The mink has already been mentioned, but another species from North America, the signal crayfish (*Pacifastacus leniusculus*) is now posing a very real threat to our native white-clawed crayfish (*Austropotamobius pallipes*). The signal crayfish was first introduced into Europe because it grows more rapidly than some of the native species and is therefore valued by those rearing crayfish commercially. Unfortunately, it brought with it a fungal infection (*Aphanomyces astaci*), the so-called crayfish plague. Whereas the signal crayfish is plague-resistant, the infection has proved fatal to some of the European species. Introduction of signal crayfish from Sweden into Britain in 1976, when juveniles were distributed to several hundred sites, has led to the elimination of the native species from many rivers in southern and eastern England in the last 20 years. Within Dorset, the native white-clawed crayfish is now restricted to the rivers Piddle, Allen and Axe.

Introduction of the signal crayfish (shown here) has had devastating consequences for the native white-clawed crayfish.

Himalayan balsam is an attractive riverside plant, but high seed production and synchronous germination results in dense stands of vegetation which compete with the native flora.

A number of invasive plants which were introduced in the last century have also spread along the banks of rivers in Britain, sometimes to the detriment of the native vegetation. Himalayan balsam (*Impatiens glandulifera*), Japanese knotweed (*Fallopia japonica*) and even giant hogweed (*Heracleum mantegazzianum*) have all been reported along watercourses within Dorset. Himalayan balsam in particular appears to be spreading, and in addition to careful monitoring, some control may be necessary in the future.

Despite the many complex problems which remain to be resolved, our local rivers are a constant source of inspiration and pleasure, just as they were to past generations. There is now good reason to believe that, through the cooperative efforts of many organisations and individuals, they can be managed in an environmentally sustainable way, for the benefit and enjoyment of future generations.

VISITING RIVERS AND STREAMS

Rivers and streams are rarely accessible along their entire lengths although progress has been made in opening up riverside paths for walkers to enjoy. Good views are also obtainable from bridges (see 'Discover Dorset' *Bridges*). All rivers and streams are potentially hazardous and care should be taken when walking along their banks. It is advisable to keep to signposted paths and to remain alert, particularly when the party includes children.

Listed below are some of the easiest places to reach riverside locations and to capture the special atmosphere of flowing water and its associated wildlife.

Key: DWT: Dorset Wildlife Trust, NT: National Trust, RSPB: Royal Society for the Protection of Birds.

RIVER ALLEN. Tributary of the R. Stour rising in the chalk of Cranborne Chase. Can be viewed from bridges at Wimborne St. Giles, Stanbridge Mill, Horton, and Witchampton but few public paths until Wimborne. Riverside walk from Walford Bridge (car park at Walford Mill) through Wimborne.

BERE STREAM. Tributary of the R. Piddle. Good access from Elder Road, Bere Regis. Raised wooden boardwalk by stream. Round walk crosses stream and passes meadows and watercress beds.

RIVER BRIT. Slow flowing West Dorset river reaching the sea at West Bay. Brit Valley Way follows the course of the river from the Beaminster area to Bridport and West Bay. Guide book available. Enjoyable round walks from Beaminster include riverside section between Beaminster and Netherbury.

RIVER CERNE. Chalk stream set in quiet valley north of Dorchester. Footpath from Cerne Abbas to Charminster follows valley. Good riverside section between Nether Cerne and Godmanstone. (DWT Headquarters nearby at Brooklands Farm, Forston).

RIVER CRANE/MOORS RIVER. Can be visited from Moors Valley Country Park. River Crane flowing south from Cranborne, widens into Crane Lake, then takes the name of Moors River with a second lake, Moors Lake, a popular part of the Park just north of the visitor centre. River flows on to join River Stour near Hurn.

DEVIL'S BROOK. Chalk stream flowing south from Ansty and joining the R. Piddle below Dewlish. Attractive walk through meadows near stream south-east of Lower Ansty village (nr. village hall).

RIVER FROME. Major Dorset river fed by the R. Hooke, Sydling Water and R. Cerne before flowing east from Dorchester through Wareham to Poole Harbour. Accessible at Maiden Newton (from walkers' car park at Rock Pit Farm, Chilfrome Lane) with watermeadows, and on the Frampton Trail at the Wren Bridge, Frampton. Riverside path through Dorchester, whilst between Dorchester and Lr. Bockhampton there is a delightful path following the river near Stinsford. Good access also at the ford and footbridge at Moreton and near the River Laboratory at East Stoke. Best of all is the Two Rivers walk at Wareham (Frome and Piddle). Park at Wareham Quay. Leaflet available. Boats from Wareham Quay and from Poole Quay to Wareham enable the tidal reaches to be enjoyed.

RIVER HOOKE. Flows through Kingcombe Meadows [DWT] and Toller Porcorum to join R. Frome at Maiden Newton. Riverside meadows are a feature of the DWT Reserve and walks are provided by the Trust and by the Kingcombe Centre. Limited parking at Pound Cottage (SY 554990).

RIVER IWERNE. Tributary of the R. Stour. Flows south from Iwerne Minster past Hambledon and Hod Hills to join R. Stour above Blandford. Visible from Shroton and from riverside path at north end of Stourpaine village.

RIVER PIDDLE. Rising in the chalk, the river flows south through Piddletrenthide to Puddletown and then turns east and flows parallel to the R. Frome towards Wareham. Can be enjoyed from the garden of Athelhampton House. Access via the Wareham Two Rivers walk at Wareham (see R. Frome above). Park in Streche Road car park and walk to Wareham Common.

SHERFORD RIVER. Flows from Bloxworth through Wareham Forest into Poole Harbour at Lytchett Bay. Visible from Sherford Bridge on B3075 south of Morden.

RIVER STOUR. Rising at Stourhead [NT] Dorset's major river flows for 75 miles south-east to the sea at Christchurch. It can be followed for its entire length on the Stour Valley Way, although the route is not always right by the river.
    The best access points include:
    Stour Provost – West Stour
    Sturminster Newton – Riverside walk upstream from the town at Sturminster Newton Mill. Small car park on A357 by the bridge. Fiddleford Mill (car parking).

Blandford (riverside car park). Crawford Bridge, Spetisbury, NT section from here to White Mill Bridge nr. Sturminster Marshall (NT car park).

Wimborne – Eyebridge, nr. Pamphill (NT car park and riverside walk with disabled access). Wimborne town (rowing boat hire).

Christchurch – Throop Mill, Iford and Christchurch Quay (pleasure boats to Tuckton and to the sea through Christchurch Harbour.)

RIVER TARRANT. Rising in Cranborne Chase the chalk stream flows south-east down a broad valley before turning south-west and, as a small river, joins the R. Stour at Tarrant Crawford, two miles south-east of Blandford. Best seen from Tarrant Monkton's packhorse bridge and watersplash.

RIVER WEY AND RADIPOLE LAKE. Short river reaching the sea through Weymouth Harbour. Notable for Radipole Lake RSPB nature reserve and swannery in the centre of Weymouth. Excellent venue for bird watching. Visitor Centre and large car park.

WRIGGLE RIVER. Tributary of the R. Yeo flowing north from the chalk hills around Batcombe through Yetminster towards Yeovil. Riverside path from Mill Farm on the south edge of Yetminster towards Chetnole.

RIVER YEO. Flows out of Dorset west of Yeovil. Fine lake adjoins the two Sherborne castles.

FURTHER READING

GENERAL

Information on the geology of Dorset may be found in: Ensom, P., *Geology* (The Dovecote Press), 1998

Dorset's rivers may be viewed from bridges, many of which are of interest in themselves. For further information see: McFetrich, D. and Parsons, J., *Bridges* (The Dovecote Press), 1998

The following book is a useful compendium of information on freshwater life for use in the field. It includes sections on algae, plants, invertebrates and freshwater vertebrates: Fitter, R. and Manuel, R., *Collins Field Guide to Freshwater Life* (Collins), 1986

Dorset Wildlife Trust has its own website (www.wildlifetrust.org.uk/dorset) with information on the Rivers and Wetland Project, the Dorset Biodiversity Strategy and a link to the Dorset Otter Group website.

The Dorset Environmental Records Centre (DERC) collates and disseminates information on the flora and fauna of Dorset. For further information see www.derc.org.uk

PLANTS

A general flora which includes good quality illustrations of water plants is: Blamey, M. and Grey-Wilson, C., *The Illustrated Flora of Britain and Northern Europe* (Hodder and Stoughton), 1989

The following pocket manual has colour photographs of aquatic plants: Spencer-Jones, D. and Wade, M., *Aquatic Plants. A guide to recognition* (ICI Professional Products), 1986

For detailed information on the distribution of plants within Dorset, including bankside and underwater species there is a recent and comprehensive publication: Bowen, H., *The Flora of Dorset* (Pisces Publications), 2000

Fitter, R. and Manuel, R., *Collins Field Guide to Freshwater Life* (Collins), (1986) provides much useful information on the invertebrate fauna of both flowing and still waters.

The publications of the Field Studies Council (www.field-studies-council.org) include a key to enable beginners to identify the main types of freshwater invertebrates: Croft, P.S., *A key to the major groups of British Freshwater Invertebrates* (An AIDGAP publication of the Field Studies Council, Taunton), 1986

For the serious investigator, the Freshwater Biological Association (FBA) publishes definitive keys to many of the major groups of freshwater invertebrates in Britain. The FBA website (www.fba.org.uk) lists all the taxonomic keys currently in print.

An up-to-date book on the identification and natural history of all the resident and migrant species of dragonflies and damselflies in Great Britain and Ireland is: Brooks, S., *Field Guide to the Dragonflies and Damselflies of Great Britain and Ireland* (British Wildlife Publishing, Hook), 2002

FISH

Again, Fitter and Manuel (1986) gives some information in field guide format, but a number of other books focus on the identification of fish.

The Field Studies Council have published an illustrated AIDGAP guide which should enable most beginners to identify freshwater fish: Wheeler, A., *Field key to the freshwater Fishes and Lampreys of the British Isles* (An AIDGAP publication of the Field Studies Council, Taunton), 1997

For a more comprehensive treatment of the freshwater fish of Britain and Europe which should appeal to the angler, naturalist and student, the following publication has colour plates and information on the identification and ecology of over 250 species of fish: Maitland, P.S., *Guide to Freshwater Fish of Britain and Europe* (Hamlyn), 2000

BIRDS

There are numerous books on the identification of birds. A recent addition to the list which includes most common birds in Britain and Ireland together with further information on their biology is: Holden, P. and Cleeves, T., *RSPB Handbook of British Birds* (Helm), 2002

Publications which offer a more comprehensive coverage of species in Europe include: Mullarney, K., Svensson, L., Zetterstrom, D. and Grant P.J., *Collins*

Bird Guide (HarperCollins), 1999 and: Jonsson, L., *Birds of Europe* (Helm), 1992

For local information, the Dorset Bird Club publishes a comprehensive Annual Report which details the species recorded in the county each year. This is supplied free to members. The club also produces an illustrated newsletter with articles and summaries of local sightings.

MAMMALS

The Dorset Otter Group website (www.dorsetottergroup.org.uk) has local information on otters and water voles, plus links to other relevant websites.

The Mammal Society website (www.abdn.ac.uk/mammal) has a wealth of interesting information, including details of publications on otters, water voles and mink.

QUALITY AND MANAGEMENT

The Wildlife Trust's Water Policy Team has its own website (www.waterpolicyteam.org) which holds a wide range of useful information on wetlands.

The Environment Agency has produced an illustrated publication describing how it contributes to wildlife conservation. This gives detailed information on the UK Biodiversity Action Plan (BAP) species and habitats for which it has taken on lead responsibility:
Environment Agency, *Focus on Biodiversity. The Environment Agency's contribution to wildlife conservation* (The Environment Agency, Bristol), 2001

The Environment Agency also produces the Local Environment Agency Plans (LEAPs) for Dorset. Copies of these Local Plans and the subsequent Annual Reviews can be obtained from: The LEAP Team, The Environment Agency, Rivers House, Sunrise Business Park, Higher Shaftesbury Road, Blandford Forum, Dorset DT11 8ST.

The CEH Dorset website (www.dorset.ceh.ac.uk) includes information on selected research projects on rivers in Dorset.

ACKNOWLEDGEMENTS

I would like to thank David Burnett of The Dovecote Press for inviting me to update and substantially enlarge what was originally a single chapter in *The Natural History of Dorset*, published by Dovecote Press in 1997. I am also grateful to Tony Bates, Chairman of the Dorset Wildlife Trust, for his practical advice and encouragement and to Bill Copland for casting his expert eye over a late draft of the manuscript and for contributing the practical section on 'Visiting Rivers and Streams'.

I am indebted to my colleagues at the Centre for Ecology and Hydrology, Dorset, for the provision of up-to-date information on a number of topics, and to Bronwen Bruce of the Dorset Wildlife Trust for checking the section on mammals. In particular, I would like to thank Tony Bates, Bob Gibbons, Mike Hammett and Colin Varndell whose superb collection of photographs greatly enhances the text.

Thanks also to Ken Ayres, Mark Brettell, the Centre for Ecology and Hydrology Dorset, Dorset County Museum, Mike Lane, and Loughborough Ecologists who supplied additional photographs. I am grateful to Christopher Chaplin for creating the map of Dorset's rivers on page 6.

I would like to thank the following for allowing the inclusion of illustrations in their possession or for which they hold the copyright: Ken Ayres; page 65: Tony Bates; pages 10, 11, 12, 13, 15 (both), 16, 17, 19, 24 (both), 35, 60, 68; Mark Brettell; page 58: Centre for Ecology and Hydrology Dorset; pages 40, 41, 62: Dorset County Museum; page 14: Bob Gibbons; front & back covers, pages 9, 20 (both), 21, 22, 23 (both), 25 (all 3), 26, 27, 34 (both), 36, 37 (bottom), 39 (right), 56, 61: Mike Lane (Natural Image); 59: Loughborough Ecologists; page 66: Colin Varndell; frontispiece, pages 37 (top), 47, 48, 49, 50, 51 (both), 52 (both), 53, 55, 57, 63: The Wildlife Photo Library UK: pages 4, 29, 30, 31, 32, 33, 39 (left), 42, 43, 44, 45 (both), 67.

Finally, I would like to thank my wife, Mavis, for accepting my preoccupation with the completion of this book with her usual understanding and good humour.

INDEX

Alder 26-28
Alderflies 29, 31, 39
Algae 20, 31
Alton Pancras 13
Ansty 70
Aquifer 10
Arrowhead 25
Athelhampton House 70
Atlantic salmon 40-44, 46

Banded demoiselle 37, 52, 53
Barbel 45-46
Barn swallow 53, 59
Bass 44
Batcombe 71
Beaminster 69
Beautiful demoiselle 37
Beetles 29
Bere Regis 13, 69
Bere stream 13, 24, 69
Biodiversity Action Plan 56, 57, 65, 66, 74
Bivalvia 29
Black poplar 16
Blackfly larvae 31, 39
Blackfly, *Metacnephia amphora* 32
Blandford fly, *Simulium posticatum* 34, 35
Blandford Forum 6, 14, 27, 35, 46, 70, 71
Bleak 46
Bloxworth 18, 70
Bournemouth 6, 64
Bovington stream 12
Bradford Peverell 9
Branched bur-reed 23
Bridport 17, 69
Brit Valley Way 69
Brook lamprey 44
Brownsea Island 54

Brown trout 4, 31, 43, 46
Bugs 29
Bullhead 31, 42, 43
Burton Bradstock 17

Caddisflies 30, 31, 33, 36, 53
Caddis larvae 29, 47
Catchment Abstraction Management Strategies 65
Caundle Brook 6, 14
Centre for Ecology and Hydrology Dorset 18, 19, 43, 74
Cerne Abbas 69
Cetti's warbler 50
Chalk rivers 66
Chalk streams 7, 8, 10, 12, 13, 21, 23, 33, 41, 43, 48, 64, 69, 70, 71
Charminster 69
Charmouth 17
Cheselbourne 13
Chetnole 71
Child Okeford 27
Chironomidae 31
Christchurch 6, 16, 17, 70, 71
Christchurch Harbour 7, 46, 50, 71
Christchurch Quay 71
Chub 46
Coleoptera 29
Common clubrush 24
Common reed 50
Convention on Biodiversity 65
Comfrey 23
Coot 50
Corfe Castle 18
Corfe River 6, 18

Cranborne 16, 69
Cranborne Chase 69, 71
Crane Lake 69
Crawford Bridge 71
Crayfish plague 32, 67
Crustacea 29

Dace 43
Damselflies 29, 34, 37, 38, 48, 53, 73
Daubenton's bat 59
Devil's Brook 13, 70
Dewlish 70
Dipper 47, 48
Diptera 30
Dorchester 6, 9, 11-13, 22, 43, 63, 69, 70
Dorset Biodiversity Strategy 72
Dorset Bird Club 74
Dorset Environmental Records Centre 59, 72
Dorset Otter Group 57, 58, 72, 74
Dorset Wildlife Trust 10, 17, 57, 58, 69, 72
Dragonflies 29, 31, 38, 53, 60, 61, 73

East Burton 14
East Stoke 18, 44, 70
Eel 46
English Nature 13, 16, 18
Environment Agency 18, 22, 33, 41, 56, 57, 62, 64-66, 74
Ephemeroptera 29
Evershot 11
Eyebridge 71

Fiddleford Mill 70
Field Studies Council 73

Fifehead Neville 15
Fisherman's mayfly,
 Ephemera danica 36
Flatworms 29, 31
Flounder 44
Flowering rush 25, 27
Fool's watercress 20, 21
Frampton 21, 70
Frampton Trail 70
Freshwater Biological
 Association 18, 73
Freshwater shrimp 30
Functional feeding groups
 30
Furzebrook 18

Gastropoda 29
Giant hogweed 68
Godmanstone 69
Goosander 54
Grannom, *Brachycentrus
 subnubilus* 36
Grayling 31, 43
Greater willowherb 23
Green sandpiper 54
Grey heron 2
Grey wagtail 48
Grilse 42

Hambledon Hill 70
Hardy's Monument 17
Hengistbury Head 17
Hemiptera 29
Himalayan balsam 68
Hirudinea 29
Hobby 53
Hod Hill 70
Horton 69
House martin 53, 59
Hurn 69

Iford 71
Imago 36
Institute of Freshwater
 Ecology 18
Institute of Terrestrial
 Ecology 18
Iwerne Minster 70

Japanese knotweed 68

Kingfisher 48, 49
Kingcombe 26

Kingcombe Centre 70
Kingcombe Meadows 70

Leeches 29, 31
Lesser water parsnip 22
Little egret 54
Little grebe 50
Local Environment
 Agency Plans 62, 74
Loddon pondweed 27
Lower Bockhampton 70
Lower Kingcombe 10
Luckford Lake 12
Lyme Regis 6
Lytchett Bay 18, 70

Maiden Newton 70
Malacostraca 29
Mammal Society 74
Mannington Brook 46
Manston Brook 14
Marsh woundwort 35
Mayflies 29, 31, 33, 36,
 38, 39, 53
Mayfly *Paraleptophlebia
 werneri*, 33
Meadowsweet 23, 35
Megaloptera 30
Melbury Park 10
Mink 59, 67
Minnow 43, 49
Moorhen 50
Moors River 6,16, 17,
 27, 33, 34, 60-62, 69
Moors Lake 69
Moors Valley Country
 Park 69
Morden 70
Moreton 70
Mussels 29
Mute swan 20, 50

National Trust 69
Natural Environment
 Research Council 18
Nether Cerne 69
Netherbury 69
Non-biting midge 31, 38
North Dorset Downs 10
North Winterbourne 6,
 11, 14
Northern lapwing 52, 53

Odonata 29
Oligochaeta 29, 31
Orange-spotted emerald
 dragonfly 61, 62
Otter 46, 55, 57-57, 66

Palmersford STW 61
Pamphill 71
Piddletrentide 70
Pike 43
Pipistrelle 59
Plecoptera 29
Poole 6, 64
Poole Harbour 7, 13, 18,
 50, 54, 70
Poole Quay 70
Pound Cottage 70
Puddletown 70
Pulham 15
Purbeck 18
Purple loosestrife 23

Radipole Lake 18, 50, 71
Redshank 52, 53
Reed canary-grass 23
Reed sweet-grass 23
Reed warbler 50, 51
R. Allen 6, 14, 46, 64,
 67, 69
R. Avon 6, 16, 17, 41,
 44, 46, 54
R. Axe 6, 17, 47, 58, 67
R. Bride 6, 17, 58
R. Brit 6, 17, 47, 58, 69
R. Cale 14
R. Cerne 6, 12, 69, 70
R. Char 6, 17, 57, 58
R. Crane 6, 16, 46, 69
R. Divelish 14, 15
R. Frome 6, 7, 9-14, 18,
 21-23, 25, 32-34, 40,
 41, 43-46, 52-54, 56-58,
 63,70
R. Hooke 6, 10, 26, 47,
 70,
R. Iwerne 70
R. Lodden 14
R. Lydden 6, 14, 15
R. Piddle 6, 7, 13, 14,
 18, 22, 23, 25, 33, 41,
 43, 44, 46, 53, 58, 64,
 67, 69, 70
R. Stour 6, 7, 11, 14-17,

22, 24, 25, 27, 33-35, 41, 44-46, 48, 49, 53, 54, 58, 62, 69-71
R. Tarrant 14, 46, 71
R. Wey 6, 17, 71
R. Win 12
R. Yeo 6, 17, 58, 71
River Laboratory 18, 19, 33, 34, 41, 42, 64, 66, 70
River lamprey 44
River Habitat Survey 66
River water dropwort 22
Rivers and Wetland Project 72
Roach 45, 46
Royal Society for the Protection of Birds 69, 71, 73

Salmon, atlantic 40-44, 46
Sand martin 53, 59
Sargasso Sea 46
Scarce-chaser dragonfly 34
Sea lamprey 44
Sea trout 41, 43, 44, 46
Sedge warbler 50, 51
Shaftesbury 6
Sherborne 6, 71
Sherford Bridge 70
Sherford River 18, 70
Shroton 70
Signal crayfish 32, 67
Simuliidae 31
Siskins 26
Site of Special Scientific Interest 13, 16, 17, 61
Smelt 44
Snails 29, 31
South Winterbourne 6, 12, 32
Southern damselfly 66
Spetisbury 71
Stanbridge Mill 69

Stanpit Marsh 17
Starwort 22
Stinsford 70
Stoneflies 29
Stone loach 43
Stour Provost 70
Stour Valley Way 70
Stourhead 14, 70
Stourpaine 70
Sturminster Marshall 22, 71
Sturminster Newton 14, 16, 70
Sturminster Newton Mill 70
Subimago 36
Summer snowflake 27
Swanage 6
Swift 53
Swineham Point 18
Sydling Water 6, 12, 70

Tadnoll Brook 12
Tarrant Crawford 71
Tarrant Monkton 71
The Fleet 17
Thick-lipped mullet 44
Thin-lipped mullet 44
Throop Mill 71
Toller Porcorum 70
Trichoptera 30
Tricladida 29
Troublefield 17
Trout brown 4, 31, 43, 46
Trout, sea 41, 43, 44, 46
True flies 30, 31, 33, 53
True worms 29, 31
Tuckton 71
Tundra swan 54

Uddens Water 16, 27, 33

Walford Bridge 69
Walford Mill 69
Wareham 6, 12, 13, 18,

22, 52, 70
Wareham Channel 18
Wareham Common 70
Wareham Forest 18, 70
Wareham Quay 70
Water Barn Mill 14
Watercress 20, 21, 23, 24
Watercress bed 24, 54, 55, 69
Water crowfoot 11, 20-22, 36, 39, 63
Water Framework Directive 64
Water policy Team 74
Water meadows 13, 14, 70
Water shrew 55
Water vole 55, 58, 59, 66
Wessex Water Services 62
West Bay 69
Weymouth 6, 17, 71
Weymouth Harbour 71
Weymouth Bay 17
White-clawed crayfish 32, 66, 67
White Mill 16, 22
White Mill Bridge 71
Wimborne Minster 6, 14, 16, 27, 46, 69, 71
Wimborne St. Giles 69
Winfrith Technology Centre 19
Winterbourne 9, 10, 20, 21, 32, 33, 64
Winterbourne Clenston 11
Witchampton 69
Wool 14
Wraxall Brook 10
Wriggle River 6, 71

Yellow water lily 25, 35
Yeovil 71
Yetminster 71

The

DISCOVER DORSET

Series of Books include

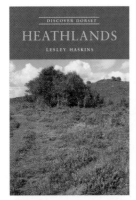

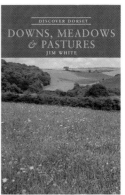

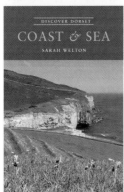

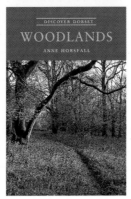

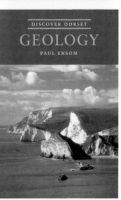

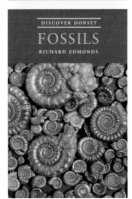

All the books about Dorset published by
The Dovecote Press
are available in bookshops throughout the
county, or in case of difficulty direct from the
publishers.
The Dovecote Press Ltd, Stanbridge,
Wimborne, Dorset BH21 4JD
Tel: 01258 840549
www.dovecotepress.com